SCHOLASTIC
Phonics

AF095826

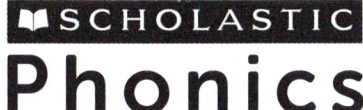

Clues for Tea

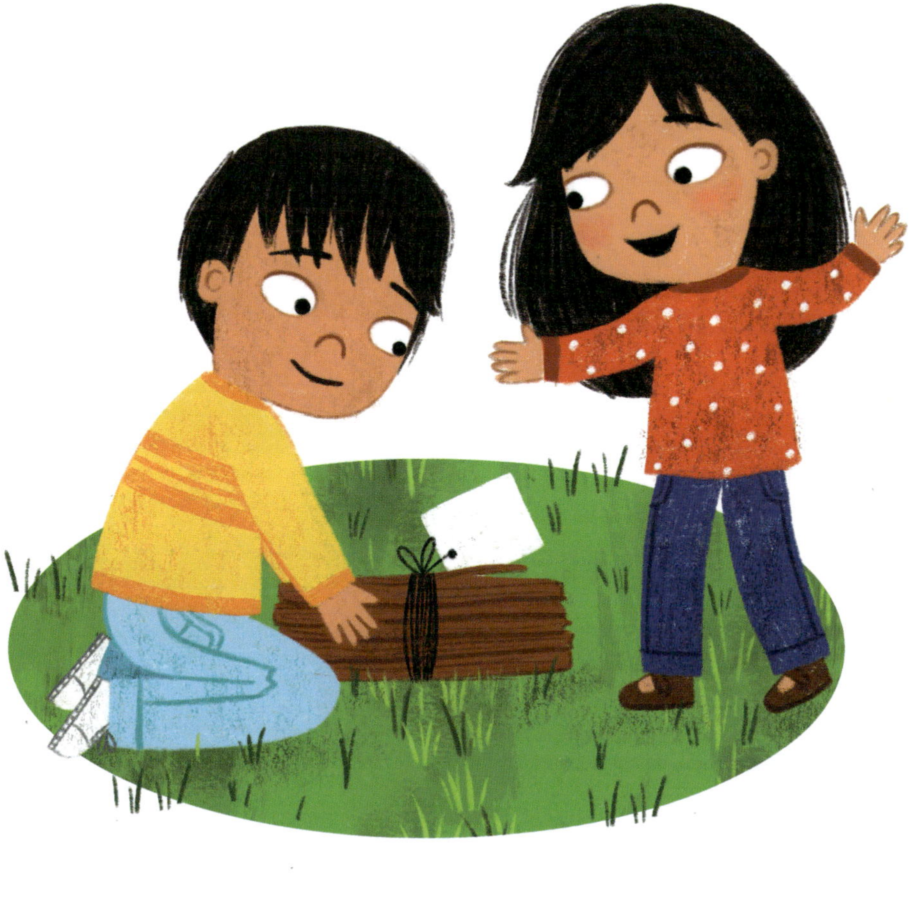

Published in the UK by Scholastic Education, 2022
Scholastic Distribution Centre, Bosworth Avenue, Tournament Fields, Warwick, CV34 6UQ
Scholastic Ireland, 89E Lagan Road, Dublin Industrial Estate, Glasnevin, Dublin, D11 HP5F

SCHOLASTIC and associated logos are trademarks and/or registered trademarks of Scholastic Inc.
www.scholastic.co.uk
© 2022 Scholastic
1 2 3 4 5 6 7 8 9   2 3 4 5 6 7 8 9 0 1

Printed by Ashford Colour Press
The book is made of materials from well-managed, FSC®-certified forests and other controlled sources.

A CIP catalogue record for this book is available from the British Library.

ISBN 978-0702-30912-0

All rights reserved. This book is sold subject to the condition that it shall not, by way of trade or otherwise, be lent, hired out or otherwise circulated in any form of binding or cover other than that in which it is published. No part of this publication may be reproduced, stored in a retrieval system, or transmitted in any form or by any other means (electronic, mechanical, photocopying, recording or otherwise) without prior written permission of Scholastic Limited.

Every effort has been made to trace copyright holders for the works reproduced in this publication, and the publishers apologise for any inadvertent omissions.

Author
Catherine Baker
Editorial team
Rachel Morgan, Vicki Yates, Fiona Undrill, Jennie Clifford
Design team
Dipa Mistry, Justin Hoffmann, Andrea Lewis, We Are Grace
Illustrations
Emma Randall/Plum Pudding Illustration

Help your child to read!

This book practises these letters and letter sounds.
Point and say the sounds with your child:

- ay (as in 'Saturday')
- ou (as in 'out')
- ea (as in 'tea')
- ir (as in 'first')
- ue (as in 'clue')

Your child may need help to read these common tricky words:

- I, to, you, some, said, me, the, of, she
- was, be, full, have, all, put, we

Before reading
- Look at the cover picture and read the title together. Read the back cover blurb to your child.
- Ask your child: *What do you think the children in the picture are doing? Have you ever tried solving a clue? What happened?*

During reading
- If your child gets stuck on a word, remind them to sound it out and then blend the sounds to read the word: c-l-ue-s, clues.
- If they are still stuck, show them how to read the word.
- Check that your child understands what the clues mean. For instance, 'stick around' means 'stay around', 'full of beans' means 'full of energy', and 'loafing around' means 'lying around lazily'.

After reading
- Ask your child: *Where did the children find the beans?*
- *Do you think it would be fun to cook your tea in the garden?*

On Saturday, May and I went to Gran's for tea.

"To win this treat, you must track down some clues!" said Gran.

"How confusing!" said May.
I led the way to the tree.

Then May shouted out, "Look!" She pointed to some sticks on the ground.

"Sticks!" I said. "The clue said, 'stick around'!" I picked up the sticks. The next clue was tied to them.

May bounded off to the tulips. She soon found the blue thing.

It was a tin of beans!

The third clue was underneath the beans.

I tried looking under a shrub near the bird feeder.

Then I shouted with joy.
I found a fresh brown loaf!

"You have found all the clues," said Gran. "Let's have tea."

Gran heaped up the sticks – and set them alight!

Then she put the beans in a pan and heated them up.

May stirred the beans.
I toasted some of the loaf!

We all enjoyed the beans on toast. "This is the best tea ever," said May.

"True," I said. "And the best clues, too!"

Retell the story